Published by Melanin Origins LLC
PO Box 122123; Arlington, TX 76012

First Edition

Library of Congress Control Number: 2019914882

ISBN: 978-1-62676-664-8 hardback
ISBN: 978-1-62676-659-4 paperback
ISBN: 978-1-62676-658-7 ebook
ISBN: 978-1-62676-588-7 Coloring Book

This book is dedicated to all the Beautiful Black Girls who never felt like they were enough. I am here to tell you that you are amazing. Beautiful Black Girl, do not let anyone ever dim your sparkle. Hold your head high and never let your crown fall. There is no greater love in the entire world than the love you have for yourself. Be unapologetically you!!

About The Author

Keshia Johnson is the Founder and CEO of Black Girls are a Movement an organization that is dedicated to empowering and equipping young girls with valuable life skills and establishing a foundation to self-love. She has a passion for helping girls reach their full potential. Ms. Johnson is an Author, Speaker, and Trainer.

CPSIA information can be obtained
at www.ICGtesting.com
Printed in the USA
LVHW070733040921
696955LV00015B/670